EXPERIMENTAL ANTENNA TOPICS

Books are to be retu... ...or
the last da... ...

Dedication

This book is dedicated to Sarah and Laura

EXPERIMENTAL ANTENNA TOPICS

by

H. C. WRIGHT

BERNARD BABANI (publishing) LTD
THE GRAMPIANS
SHEPHERDS BUSH ROAD
LONDON W6 7NF
ENGLAND

© 1990 BERNARD BABANI (publishing) LTD

First Published — February 1990

British Library Catalogue in Publication Data
Wright, H. C.
    Experimental antenna topics
    1. Antennas. Design
    I. Title
    621.38'028'3

ISBN 0 85934 223 9

Printed and bound in Great Britain by Cox & Wyman Ltd, Reading

Preface

Although nearly a century has passed since Marconi's first demonstrations of radio communication, there is still research and experiment to be carried out in the field of antenna design and behaviour.

The aim of the experimenter will be to make a measurement or confirm a principle, and this can be done with relatively fragile, short-life apparatus. Because of this, devices described in this book make liberal use of cardboard, cooking foil, plastic bottles, cat food tins, etc. These materials are, in general, cheap to obtain and easily worked with simple tools, encouraging the trial-and-error philosophy which leads to innovation and discovery.

Although primarily a practical book with text closely supported by diagrams, some formulae which can be used by straightforward substitution and some simple graphs have also been included.

I would like to acknowledge the hospitality of the Open University Library and the help of the staff while writing this book. I am very grateful to Mr B. C. Pope for his fast and painstaking proof reading.

H. C. Wright

Warning

The young and less experienced experimenter should test and measure the antennas described here using battery-operated equipment. Mains-driven apparatus should be left for the mature expert.

Note

The symbol λ is used throughout this book to denote wavelength.

Table of Contents

Page

1. The Abe Lincoln Antenna

The Abe Lincoln is, in effect, a slot antenna curved into a cylinder in order to make it less directional than the conventional slot or dipole.

Figure 1(a) shows the dimensions of the antenna in terms of the radiation wavelength λ. The position of the antenna lead along the slot length (shown as 0.025λ from one end) determines the impedance of the antenna and may be varied to suit the input circuit.

Figure 1(b) shows the polar diagram of a 515 MHz example made from thin card covered with aluminium cooking foil. Slotted cat-food tins from which the top and bottom have been removed should give a more rugged device working at about 700 MHz.

It must be remembered that a slot antenna is polarised at right angles to the long axis of the slot.

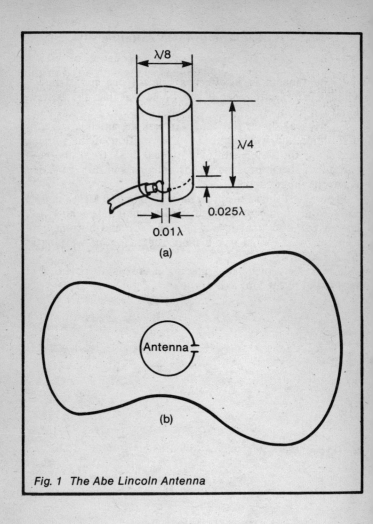

Fig. 1 The Abe Lincoln Antenna

2

2. Antenna Impedance Modification

The basic half-wave dipole has an impedance of $\sim$75 Ω. Figure 2(a) shows such an antenna made with a rod or tube having a radius r_1 and a length $\lambda/2$. If a second element of length $\lambda/2$ and radius r_2 is joined to it at a distance s, as shown in Figure 2(b), the original 75 Ω is multiplied by a factor M equal to:

$$\left(\frac{\log_{10} s/r_1}{\log_{10} s/r_2} + 1 \right)^2$$

M has a value of 4 if $r_1 = r_2$ or, alternatively, if r_1 and r_2 are both much smaller than s.

Adding a second element symmetrically (Fig.2(c)) makes M equal to:

$$\left(\frac{2 \log_{10} s/r_1}{\log_{10} s/2r_2} + 1 \right)^2$$

Three elements added symmetrically (Fig.2(d)) make the multiplying factor:

$$\left(\frac{3 \log_{10} s/r_1}{\log_{10} s/3r_2} + 1 \right)^2$$

In general for n elements added, M becomes:

$$\left(\frac{n \log_{10} s/r_1}{\log_{10} s/nr_2} + 1 \right)^2$$

This general form that M takes with a multi-element addition is sketched in Figure 2(e) for three values of n when $r_1 = r_2$. It can be seen that as s gets large, M tends to the value $(n + 1)^2$. (The apparent zero value of M given when $s^{(n+1)} = nr_1nr_2$ cannot be physically realised as s must be greater than $r_1 + r_2$.)

3

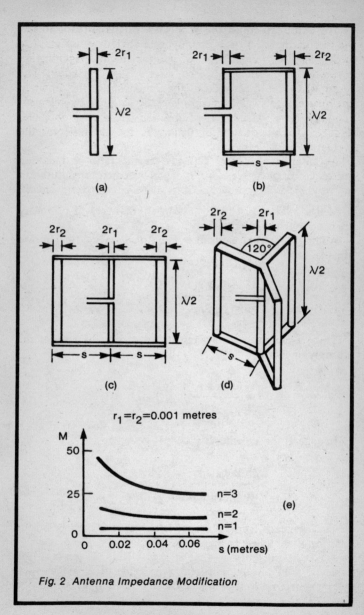

Fig. 2 Antenna Impedance Modification

4

The ability to adjust the impedance of the antenna to suit the circuit in which it is employed is obviously useful. The most common exploitation of multi-element magnification occurs when a reflector is used, as in a Yagi-Uda array. The action of the reflector reduces the impedance of the dipole to one-quarter of its value when isolated. By using a two element assembly an imedpedance of 4 x 75 Ω can be obtained. Reduced to one-quarter of this value by the reflector the standard 75 Ω is retrieved.

As antenna efficiency depends on the ratio of radiation resistance to ohmic resistance, a multi-element structure can be very effective, provided it is matched into its circuit.

3. Between Antennas

The results from experiments with widely-separated antennas will be very dependent on the behaviour of the radio signal as it travels between transmitter and receiver.

There are two principal forms of signal propagation: the ground-wave and the sky-wave.

The ground-wave follows the earth's surface and has a comparatively short range. Part of its electric field travels slowly in the ground (or the sea) lagging behind that part above the surface and so tilting the wave forward as shown in Figure 3(a). The retarding effect of the ground or sea increases with the frequency of the radiation so the tilt increases also, leading to a rapid absorption of higher frequency signals. Figure 3(b) shows a plot of ground-wave range versus frequency.

The sky-wave depends on the reflection of the signal from one of two layers of free electrons that exist round the earth. These act on the radio wave rather as a slab of glass would on a ray of light. Striking the layer of electrons at a low angle the wave is merely deflected, but at a large angle it is reflected back as shown in Figure 3(c). (Section 18 gives a mathematical treatment of this behaviour of free electron layers.)

The lower of the two layers is about 70 miles high and mainly affects signals with frequencies below 1 MHz. This is the Kennelly-Heaviside (E) layer. The upper, or Appleton (F), layer is about 170 miles high and reflects waves of frequency between 1 and 3 or 4 MHz. Both layers are formed by radiation from the sun or outer space, freeing electrons from molecules of air and other gases.

Figure 3(d) sketches ground and sky wave behaviour. The region marked A—B is called the dead space, being beyond the ground-wave range but less than the reflected sky-wave travel. No signal can be received in this region.

As the layers are produced partly by solar radiation they will start to decay in the hours of darkness, the lowest part of a layer disappearing first. This causes the layers to become higher in effect and the reflected distance becomes greater as shown in Figure 3(e). The increase in remote radio stations

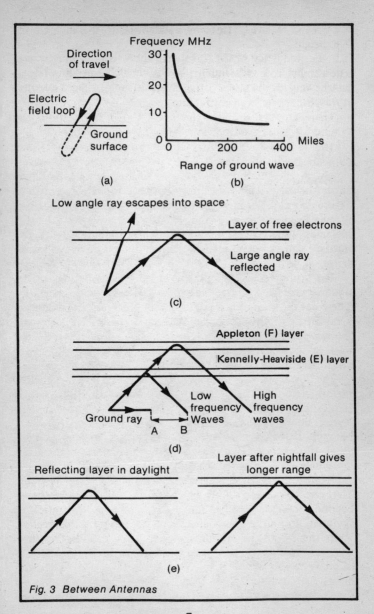

Direction of travel →

Electric field loop

Ground surface

(a)

Frequency MHz

Range of ground wave

Miles

(b)

Low angle ray escapes into space

Layer of free electrons

Large angle ray reflected

(c)

Appleton (F) layer

Kennelly-Heaviside (E) layer

Ground ray

Low frequency Waves

High frequency waves

A ← → B

(d)

Reflecting layer in daylight

Layer after nightfall gives longer range

(e)

Fig. 3 Between Antennas

that can be received after nightfall is due to this increase in layer height.

If the frequency of the signal is in the U.H.F. or microwave region it behaves very much like visible light, needing transmitting and receiving antennas to be in line of sight of one another.

4. Cold Antennas

The efficiency of a receiving antenna is the ratio of the power it passes to its input circuit compared to the total power it absorbs from the radiation falling on it. For a transmitting antenna this becomes the ratio of radiated power to the power fed into the antenna. For both transmission and reception the efficiency depends on the electrical, or ohmic, resistance R_E and the radiation resistance R_R of the antenna. In short:

Efficiency E = (Power to circuit)/(power absorbed)

   or (Power radiated)/(power fed in)

   = $R_R/(R_R + R_E)$ $\rightarrow$ =0 : 100% efficiency

E obviously increases as R_E, the electrical resistance, gets smaller and one way of decreasing R_E is by reducing the temperature. Figure 4(a) shows how the resistance of a copper wire having a room temperature value of 1 ohm changes with temperature. These small changes in R_E would not have a large effect on efficiency if the radiation resistance were to have its usual 75 ohms value, but an antenna deliberately made to have a small radiation resistance would magnify the effect. One way in which a low radiation resistance can be very simply produced is to reduce the size of a dipole to much less than its normal half-wavelength value. Figure 4(b) shows the effect that such size reduction has on the radiation resistance.

The most dramatic efficiency change occurs when an antenna made from a conducting ceramic material is cooled to the temperature of liquid nitrogen and becomes superconducting. In this state all electrical resistance disappears and the antenna becomes 100% efficient. Although superconducting materials and temperatures are not easily accessible to the amateur, the signs are that they will eventually become commonplace.

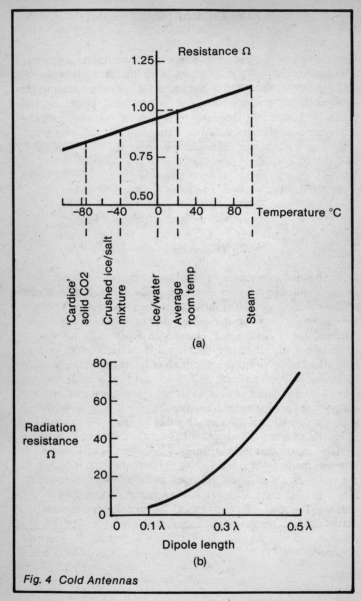

Fig. 4 Cold Antennas

10

5. The Crossed Field Antenna

The radio wave, like all electromagnetic radiation, consists of magnetic and electric fields at right angles to one another each rising regularly to a maximum in one direction and then falling to zero before rising to a maximum in the opposite direction, Figure 5(a).

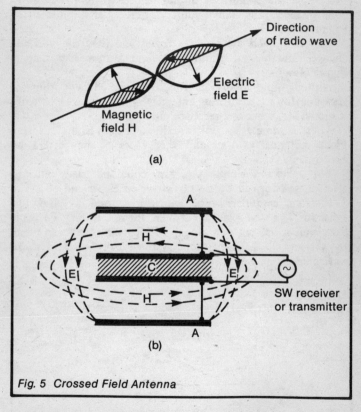

Fig. 5 *Crossed Field Antenna*

Most antennas use straight conductors designed to produce the varying electric field and let the magnetic behaviour look after itself or, less commonly, use a loop designed to produce

11

or detect the magnetic field.

A recently (1989) patented experimental antenna producing both electric and magnetic fields at right angles has been reported as efficient, and also, as insensitive to the dimensions of the structure.

This "Crossed Field Antenna" is sketched in Figure 5(b). Two metal electrodes A, connected to a radio frequency source (or receiver) produce the varying electric field E, while the displacement current in the parallel plate capacitor C, connected to the same source or receiver produces the magnetic field H.

The two fields are at right angles and they rise, fall and change direction to produce a field system like that in Figure 5(a).

Although the theory has been considered here from the viewpoint of a transmitting antenna, by the reciprocity theory it should also work as a receiving antenna.

There is some argument as to how, or even if, the "Crossed Field Antenna" works and this waits to be settled by experiment.

For a start a simple structure could be tried with the electrodes A formed by tin lids stuck on either end of a 4 to 5 cm long cardboard tube which is slotted to allow the capacitor C to be placed between them. C may be made from similar lids with an air gap of a cm or so between them. By varying all the dimensions systematically a useful short-wave antenna may be made.

6. The Dielectric Clad Antenna

When a radio wave travels in a material with a dielectric constant greater than one its speed is reduced and, consequently, its wavelength is shortened. Thus for instance a half-wave dipole clad in such a dielectric material is smaller than a bare-wire antenna.

Unfortunately all real dielectric materials are lossy and absorb some signal energy producing useless heat, but where a full size antenna is too large for convenience this loss may be offset by the improved "electrical" size of the clad antenna.

An experimental, and approximate, expression for the increase in electrical length when a thin rod is clad in dielectric material is given by

$$R \approx 1 + 2\left(\frac{\sqrt{\epsilon} \cdot d}{\lambda}\right)$$

R is the ratio of the electrical/geometrical length.
ϵ is the relative dielectric constant of the cladding.
d is the thickness of the cladding.
λ is free-space wavelength.

Water is a convenient experimental material having a dielectric constant of ~80 and being easily shaped into cylindrical form by containing vessels. It is then, interesting to test the formula quoted, by considering the length of rod necessary for a quarter-wave element working at a TV frequency of 500 MHz when it is immersed in a bottle of water.

We have ϵ = 80, d is, say, 8cm, and the free-space wavelength is 60 cm.

Using these values R is found to be ~3.4 and so a quarter wave element would be about 4.5 cm.

An experimental form of water-clad antenna made using a plastic water bottle and some cooking foil is shown in Figure 6(a). Pure distilled water is desirable but tap water will demonstrate the effect.

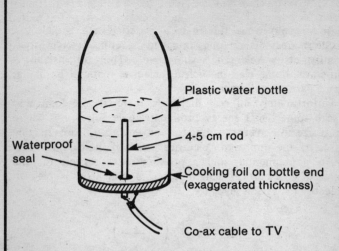

Plastic water bottle

4-5 cm rod

Waterproof seal

Cooking foil on bottle end (exaggerated thickness)

Co-ax cable to TV

(a) Water-clad ¼ Wavelength Antenna

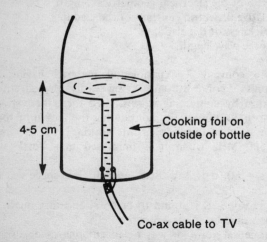

4-5 cm

Cooking foil on outside of bottle

Co-ax cable to TV

(b) Water-clad Abe Lincoln Antenna

Fig. 6 Dielectric Clad Antennas

The slot antenna can also be reduced in size by forming it on a dielectric backing. The Abe Lincoln antenna in particular could be formed by making the slot from cooking foil pasted onto a plastic water container as in Figure 6(b).

Professional work in this field has used Barium/Strontium Titanate as a dielectric material, either in powder form or fired into a ceramic shape.

7. Doubly Fed Co-Ax Antennas

Engineers at Birmingham University have developed two forms of antenna with heights of $\lambda/7$ and $\lambda/11$.

Although the designs give resonant structures despite being much smaller than the standard half-wave dipole, they suffer from a reduced radiation resistance compared with the normal 75 ohm value. This decreases their efficiency and necessitates a matching low resistance value for the antenna circuit.

The antennas are made from co-ax cable folded into U shapes with the dimensions and connections shown in the figure. Antenna as shown in Figure 7(a) has a radiation resistance of ~15 ohms and the short-circuited version shown in Figure 7(b) one of ~5 ohms.

The ground planes can be mesh or foil sheets with linear dimensions of a wavelength or so, connected to the sheath of a co-ax lead to the antenna.

As always the dimensions cited should be regarded as starting points for experimental variation.

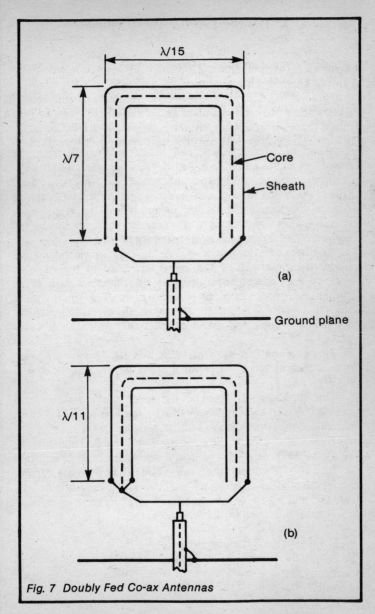

Fig. 7 Doubly Fed Co-ax Antennas

17

8. Frequency Independent Antennas

A single frequency antenna has dimensions defined in terms of its working wavelength. For example, the design for a 1 metre Yagi-Uda array would be the same as that for a 10 metre array when the element sizes are expressed in terms of wavelength.

Because of this, the design of an antenna which is to be independent of frequency, and hence wavelength, must be based on angles and ratios and not on lengths. The fundamental frequency independent antenna (F.I.A.) is formed from two cones of any convenient angle A, Figure 8(a). In theory the cones should be infinitely tall to respond to infinitely low frequencies. In practice they are made tall enough to work with the lowest frequency used.

Another basic form of F.I.A. is the logarithmic spiral where the radius R of the spiral is related to the angle of rotation θ by the equation $\log_e R = K\theta$, the constant K being chosen for convenience by the designer. The spiral should thicken uniformly along its length, as shown in Figure 8(b). The spiral is mounted on, but insulated from, a metal earth plane.

This antenna can be made directional by "pulling it out" into a conical spiral, directional along its axis, as illustrated by Figure 8(c).

The conical spiral can be flattened into a zig-zag form defined by the two angles C and B, see Figure 8(d). Again the angles are at the disposal of the designer.

The most common F.I.A. is the Log Periodic Dipole Array as shown in Figure 8(e), a design using one angle D and one length ratio W greater than one. Note that alternate dipoles are connected in opposition thus cancelling radiation to the side and making the array directional along its axis.

The symbols used in the diagram are:

I_n the length of the n'th dipole
R_n the distance of the n'th dipole from P
S_n the gap in the centre of the n'th dipole
d_n the diameter of the n'th dipole.

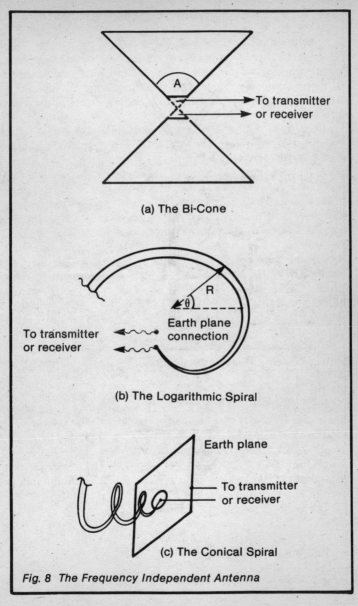

(a) The Bi-Cone

(b) The Logarithmic Spiral

(c) The Conical Spiral

Fig. 8 The Frequency Independent Antenna

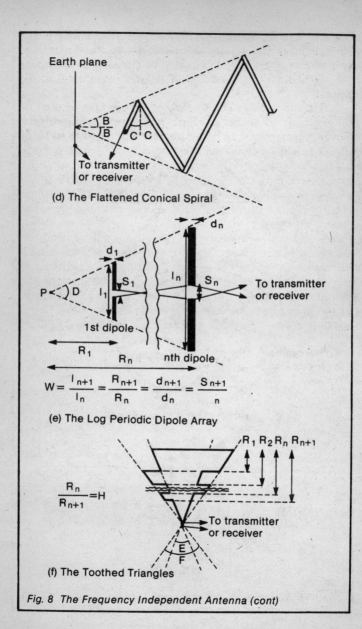

(d) The Flattened Conical Spiral

$$W = \frac{l_{n+1}}{l_n} = \frac{R_{n+1}}{R_n} = \frac{d_{n+1}}{d_n} = \frac{S_{n+1}}{n}$$

(e) The Log Periodic Dipole Array

$$\frac{R_n}{R_{n+1}} = H$$

(f) The Toothed Triangles

Fig. 8 The Frequency Independent Antenna (cont)

20

In use the dipole most nearly ½ wavelength long is the active member and adjacent elements act to some extent as the elements in a Yagi-Uda array. The designer has the values of E, W and the total number of dipoles to be used, at his disposal.

A flat approach to the bi-cone of Figure 8(a) consists of two opposing triangular elements. As with the bi-cone true frequency independence would require the triangles to be of infinite height. Failing this their "electrical" length is made as great as possible by slowing down the current flow by cutting teeth into them. Figure 8(f) shows an example where the design is defined by two angles F and E and the length ratio H which is greater than one. All four constants are at the designer's disposal.

It is seen that the concept of an F.I.A. really depends on having a structure that is large compared with any wavelength that may be used, and of a form that allows the radiating or receiving activity to be concentrated on that part of the antenna which offers resonance at the working wavelength. In the absence of infinitely large antennas there can be no true frequency-independent-antennas; only wide-band devices.

9. Gain and Efficiency

The gain and the efficiency of an antenna are two distinct and equally important characteristics.

The gain depends on the radiation power collected compared with that which a standard half-wave dipole would collect in the same radiation field. It is usually expressed in decibels and, written in full, is:

$$\text{Gain} = 10 \times \log_{10} \left\{ \frac{(\text{Power collected by antenna})}{(\text{Power collected by standard dipole})} \right\}$$

This rather clumsy expression is the standard form for antenna gain. The gain is closely linked to the directionality of the antenna. If it radiates into, or receives from, a cone with an angle A then, as A gets bigger, the gain gets smaller. At first this seems to be the wrong way round, but it can be understood by considering a dish reflector used with an antenna. The bigger the dish the more nearly parallel is the transmitted radiation. This corresponds to a small value of A, see Figure 9(a). However the bigger the dish then the greater is the amount of radiation collected also, and so the greater the gain.

In contrast to the gain, which is concerned with how much radiation power is collected, the efficiency is concerned with how much of that power is wasted and how much is made available at the antenna terminals. This can be written:

$$\text{Efficiency} = \frac{(\text{Power available at antenna terminals})}{(\text{Total power collected})}$$

It is perhaps helpful to think of the antenna as an a.c. generator with an internal resistance R_L representing the source of power loss in the antenna. This is connected to the "useful" radiation resistance R_R, as illustrated by Figure 9(b). The total power in the circuit is proportional to the gain G. The useful fraction of this is $R_R/(R_R + R_L)$ and so the antenna output is proportional to:

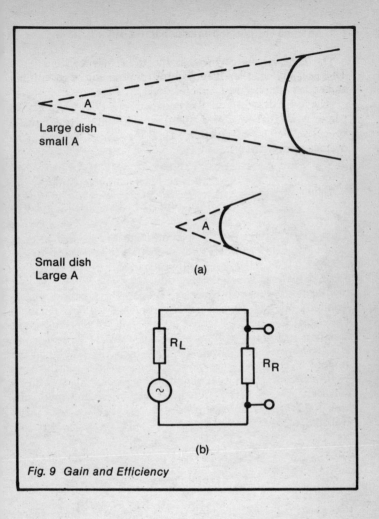

Large dish
small A

(a)

Small dish
Large A

R_L

R_R

(b)

Fig. 9 Gain and Efficiency

$$G \times \frac{R_R}{(R_R + R_L)}$$

The fraction $R_R/(R_R + R_L)$ is the efficiency and so finally:

Antenna Output is proportional to Gain × Efficiency

The same values for the gain and the efficiency hold for a given antenna whether it is used for transmission or reception.

10. Helical Antennas

If a length of wire is wound into a helix and used as an antenna it will radiate and receive at right angles to its axis if the total length of the wire used is much less than one wavelength, or it will radiate and receive along its axis if the wire length is much greater than one wavelength, as illustrated by Figure 10(a).

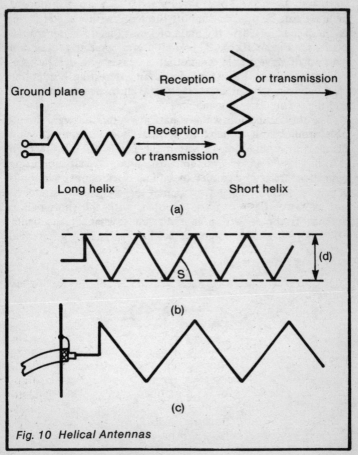

Fig. 10 Helical Antennas

The three numbers defining a helical antenna are:

L the total length of conductor used
    (not the length of the helix)
d the diameter of the helix; and
s the pitch of the helix.

These are shown on Figure 10(b).

In the first case take a "long" helix. Experiments could start with $L \sim 5\lambda$, $d \sim \lambda/3$ and $s \sim 10°$. A stout cardboard cylinder can be used to support the helix with a metal plate, or mesh, connected to the braid of a co-ax lead for the ground plane, see Figure 10(c). This should give some ten times gain over a half wave dipole, a gain that increases with decreasing s.

The action of the long helix is an interesting border-line case between that of a waveguide (as in microwave practice) and that of an orthodox antenna.

The short helical antenna is basically a quarter wave monopole wound into a helix to shorten it for convenience in portable or mobile use. A reasonable gain is still possible even if L has less than its optimum $\lambda/4$ value. A self-supporting wire structure can be formed by coiling thick copper wire onto a pencil. Removed from the pencil the coil can be stretched out as far as desired. The problem with the short helical antenna is the reduction in radiation resistance, and hence efficiency, it shows compared with a full size $\lambda/4$ antenna.

11. Inductance Design

The unit of inductance is the henry but this is so large that most texts deal in microhenrys, the one millionth part of the henry. The symbol for the microhenry is μH.

The inductance L of a long, thin coil is given by the formula:

$$L = (K.N^2 D^2)/\ell \ \mu H$$

Here N is the number of turns on the coil
D is the diameter of the coil in metres
ℓ is the length of the coil in metres
K is the permeability of the core material equal to 1 for air.

This formula is accurate if ℓ is much greater than D.

For a short coil a correction factor must be used. Where a winding of thickness d is used on a short coil, as in the Figure 11, the inductance L is given by:

$$L = K.N^2(D - d).F \ \mu H$$

where F is a correction factor depending on the magnitude of $(D - d)/(\ell + d)$. F can be read from the graph.

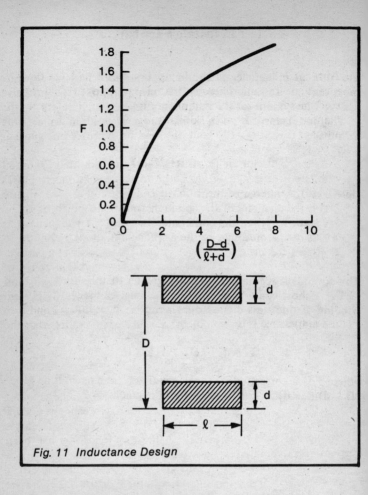

Fig. 11 Inductance Design

12. Interference Effects

Note: It is unfortunate that "interference" has two separate meanings in radio science. It can be applied to intrusive electrical noise or static, but in this section it refers to the manner in which two similar radio waves can cancel one another if they are $180°$ out of phase, or reinforce one another if they are in phase.

When radiation falls on a slit or aperture that is broad compared with the wavelength of the radiation, it passes straight through with no change of direction, see Figure 12(a). If the width of the slit is made so small as to be comparable with the wavelength then the slit will behave as a radiating source, see Figure 12(b). This allows radiation to be focussed by using a number of narrow slits set at a particular distance apart. In Figure 12(c) the three rays that converge on F from the parallel radiation falling on the slits S_1, S_0 and S_1^1 will reinforce one another if the distances $S_1.F$, and $S_1^1.F$ are one wavelength greater than $S_0.F$. This condition of constructive interference between the rays requires that the slit separation h satisfies:

$$h^2/S_0.F \sim 2\lambda$$

By making the central slit a circular disc and the outer slits into a ring or annulus a conventional circular lens known as a Fresnel Zone Plate is formed. This type of lens is commonly used with visible light and focussing has been demonstrated with microwave radiation.

An interesting experiment would be to examine the effect at TV wavelengths. If the outer slits of Figure 12(c) are set 1.5 metres from the central slit, a half-wave dipole some two metres from the slit system should receive a focussed signal. The slits must be parallel with the direction of polarisation of the television signal. Alternatively if the experiment is made with the 2.7 cm radiation of satellite TV a much less cumbersome slit system results with all distances divided by about 20.

The interference effect on signal strength when certain parts of a beam of radiation are blocked, not only occurs for

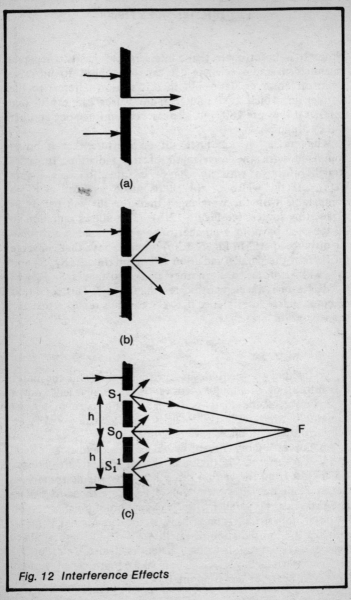

Fig. 12 Interference Effects

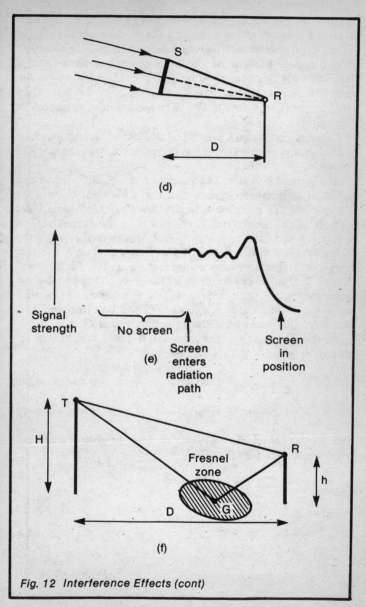

(d)

Signal strength

No screen

(e)

Screen enters radiation path

Screen in position

Fresnel zone

(f)

Fig. 12 Interference Effects (cont)

systems of slits but can be shown when a single circular screen is placed between the receiver and the incoming radiation. In Figure 12(d) the circular screen S is introduced into radiation from a remote transmitter. With the screen a distance D from the receiver R its radius must be $\sqrt{D.\lambda}$. As it enters the radiation path the signal strength will at first oscillate, then rise to a peak and finally fall to a minimum as suggested in Figure 12(e).

Cooking foil should provide a satisfactory screen material and again, the experiment is less cumbersome with the satellite radiation.

The ground is in general a good reflector of radio waves and radiation reflected from a central point between transmitter and receiver can interfere with the direct ray. In Figure 12(f) a ray from the transmitter T reflected from the ground at G to a receiver R travels a distance ~ 4 H.h/D farther than the direct ray. If this value of 4 H.h/D is equal to λ the two signals will reinforce one another, if equal to $\lambda/2$ they will cancel. It is sufficient for some interference to happen if these relationships are only approximately true. Because of this, reflection from an area surrounding G will be effective. This area is roughly oval and is known as the Fresnel Zone.

If the formula for the two interference conditions are written in terms of the receiver height h:

$$h_{MAX} = D.\lambda/4.H \qquad \text{for a maximum}$$

and $$\qquad h_{MIN} = D.\lambda/8.H \qquad \text{for a minimum}$$

and so the separation between receiver heights for a maximum and a minimum is

$$D.\lambda/8.H$$

13. Long and Short Dipoles

The standard half-wave dipole consists of a straight conductor just less than half a wavelength long, broken at the centre to take the lead from the signal as shown in Figure 13(a). Such a dipole mounted at least three wavelengths above the ground would behave like a pure 75 ohm resistor without inductance or capacitance. This 75 ohms can be increased by moving the point at which the lead is introduced towards the end of the antenna, see Figure 13(b).

If for any reason, the dipole has to be reduced in length below 0.48λ it will behave as though a capacitor were added to the resistance. This capacity can be removed by making the dipole longer electrically than it is physically. One method of doing this is discussed in the section on dielectric-clad antennas but it may also be done by introducing an inductance into each arm of the dipole. Experiment could start with inductances formed by winding some ten turns of wire onto a pencil with a tapping point taken at each turn. With a coil placed in each arm symmetrical tapping points can be chosen for maximum signal, as illustrated by Figure 13(c). If the signal shows an increase right up to the point when all the turns of the coil are in circuit then coils of larger diameter should be wound and tried. If the signal increases up to the point when only one turn is in use, then smaller diameter coils should be tried.

If the dipole length is greater than 0.48λ then it will behave as an inductance. This is a less common problem than the short dipole but it has the obvious remedy of putting series capacitors in each arm, see Figure 13(d). Variable capacitors of 500 pF, preferably ganged together, should be tried.

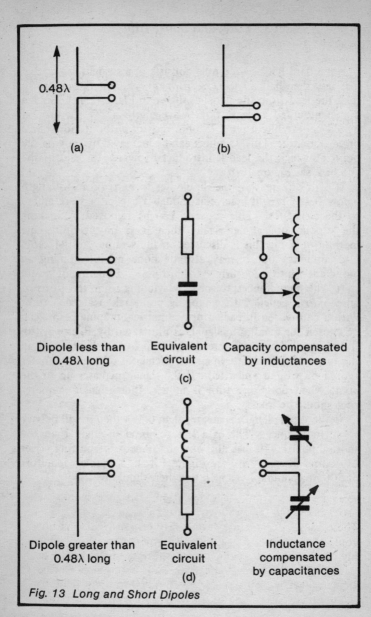

0.48λ

(a) (b)

Dipole less than 0.48λ long

Equivalent circuit

Capacity compensated by inductances

(c)

Dipole greater than 0.48λ long

Equivalent circuit

Inductance compensated by capacitances

(d)

Fig. 13 Long and Short Dipoles

34

14. Loop and Frame Antennas

A resonant single-turn loop antenna for use with V.H.F. or U.H.F. radiation is of a reasonable size for domestic use. Such loops have been reported as giving 10 times the signal obtained from a simple half-wave dipole. The loop should be in the form of a circle with a diameter of between 1/3 and 1/2 a wavelength. One end of a gap in the loop is connected to the sheath of a co-ax cable, the other to the core. It is mounted about 1/4 of a wavelength above a large area metal ground plane, both the loop diameter and the height above the ground plane being varied experimentally to find the best values, see Figure 14(a).

When working in the medium and long wave regions any practical loop or frame antenna will be small compared with a wavelength. The undesirable result of this is a low radiation resistance for the antenna. If n turns of wire are wound onto a frame having an area of A square metres as shown in Figure 14(b) the radiation resistance will be:

$$1.6 \times 10^4 \ (nA/\lambda^2)^2 \ \text{ohms} \ .$$

It will have the same effective length as a straight wire antenna of length:

$$2\pi nA/\lambda \ \text{metres} \ .$$

Calculating the radiation resistance and effective length for a real case will give an idea of the characteristics of a medium or long wave frame antenna. Suppose 50 turns are wound on a square of 0.5 metre side and used at 500 metres wavelength (600 kHz). The radiation resistance would be 4×10^{-5} ohms and the effective length 16 cms.

These values do not make for a very efficient antenna but it would have the advantage, like all frame antennas, of being highly directional, receiving or transmitting signals only at right angles to the axis of the frame. This property can be particularly useful after dark when radio stations tend to crowd the wave-bands.

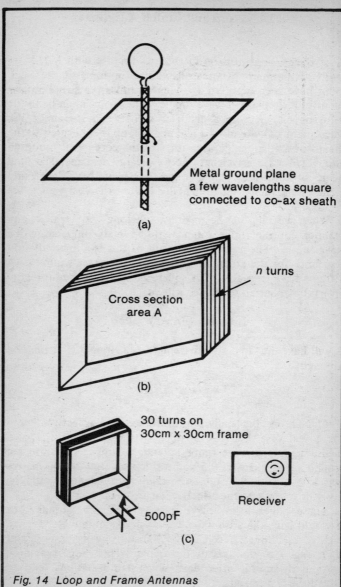

(a)

n turns

Cross section
area A

(b)

30 turns on
30cm x 30cm frame

500pF

Receiver

(c)

Metal ground plane
a few wavelengths square
connected to co-ax sheath

Fig. 14 Loop and Frame Antennas

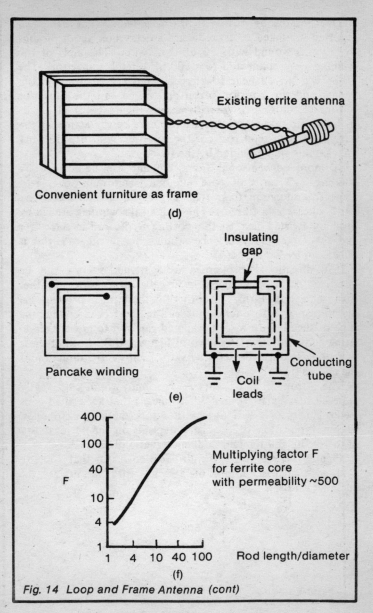

Existing ferrite antenna

Convenient furniture as frame

(d)

Insulating gap

Pancake winding

Conducting tube

Coil leads

(e)

Multiplying factor F for ferrite core with permeability ~500

F

Rod length/diameter

(f)

Fig. 14 Loop and Frame Antenna (cont)

37

One interesting form of frame antenna that has been reported consisted of a cardboard grocery box about 30 cms by 30 cms wound with 30 turns of wire. The ends of the winding were connected to a 500 pF variable capacitor. The frame was placed near to a receiver but not electrically connected and the position of set and frame and the capacitor setting all adjusted for best signal, see Figure 14(c). It needs to be set up using a weak station otherwise the action of the automatic gain control on the receiver will obscure any increase in signal provided by the frame.

A more conventional frame antenna can be formed by winding 2—3 turns of wire round a frame with an area of some two square metres. (One experimenter used a convenient bookcase as a frame.) The ends of the winding are led by ordinary twisted flex to the existing ferrite rod in a receiver and the flex is looped once around the ferrite rod, this is illustrated by Figure 14(d).

The directional properties of a frame antenna can be improved by winding the wire in a flat pancake form rather than in a box form. Another method of improving the directionality is to enclose the coil in an earthed conducting tube or sheath with a well-insulated gap in it to prevent circulating eddy currents, as shown in Figure 14(e). Both of these techniques reduce the sensitivity to signals in the direction of the coil's axis.

The introduction of a ferrite core into a coil can greatly increase the signal from it. This means that very small coils having such cores can form satisfactory miniature antennas. The multiplication of the signal depends on the permeability of the ferrite and the length/diameter ratio of the rod.

Figure 14(f) shows the multiplication factor that a ferrite core with a permeability of 500 has with various length/diameter ratios.

15. Matching and Balancing

A problem with experimental antennas, or indeed any antenna, lies in matching the antenna to its circuit so that power is not reflected back from the circuit, if receiving, or back from the antenna, if transmitting.

If the impedance of the antenna consists of a resistance plus a reactance then the circuit must have an equal resistance and an equal and opposite reactance. Opposite, as regards the reactance, means that a capacitive antenna must have an inductive circuit and vice-versa.

If these conditions are not satisfied extra impedances have to be introduced between the antenna and its circuit as shown in Figure 15(a). The values of the impedances Z_p and Z_s are:

$$Z_p = \sqrt{Z_c(Z_c - Z_A)}$$

$$Z_s = Z_A \sqrt{Z_c/(Z_c - Z_A)}$$

where Z_A is the antenna impedance and Z_c is the circuit impedance.

The two impedances can be introduced very neatly by the technique known as stub matching shown in Figure 15(b). A distance A along the line connecting antenna and circuit, a short stub of line length B, is connected across the line. The length of line A acts as the series impedance Z_s and the length B as the parallel impedance Z_p in Figure 15(a). The values of these impedances depend on the lengths A and B and, in the case of the latter, on whether the end is short-circuited or open-circuited.

The lengths A and B are usually found by experiment but a guide to the behaviour of short lengths of transmission line when used as impedance is given in Table 15.1. Here λ' is the wavelength of the radiation in the line which is usually shorter than the free-space wavelength.

Another problem occurs when an antenna having two similar elements, as in a half-wave dipole, is connected to its circuit by coaxial cable. Ideally one current I flows in the central core, while an equal current flows in the opposite

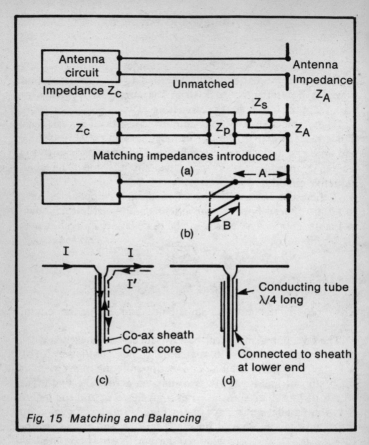

Fig. 15 Matching and Balancing

direction in the sheath as shown in Figure 15(c). However, because the sheath is usually earthed a second unwanted current I′ flows to earth in it. To choke off this undesired current the cable can be surrounded with a quarter wavelength conducting tube connected to the sheath at its lower end as in Figure 15(d). This then forms an infinite impedance for the radio-frequency currents, stopping the undesired current flow. The tube can be formed from cooking foil or, more elegantly, by painting the outer insulation of the coaxial cable with conducting silver paint.

The device is called a 'balun' as it is used to link the **bal**anced electrodes of the antenna to the **un**balanced leads of the cable.

Table 15.1

Length of short-circuited transmission line	Form of Impedance
$0 - (\lambda'/4)$	Inductive
$(\lambda'/4)$	Resistive
$(\lambda'/4) - (\lambda'/2)$	Capacitive
$(\lambda'/2) - (3\lambda'/4)$	Inductive
$(3\lambda'/4)$	Resistive
Length of open-circuited transmission line	
$0 - (\lambda'/4)$	Capacitive
$(\lambda'/4) - (\lambda'/2)$	Inductive
$(\lambda'/2)$	Resistive
$(\lambda'/2) - (3\lambda'/4)$	Capacitive

16. The Phased Array

A simple phased array could be made from two antennas a set distance apart, each fed from the same transmitter or receiver. The distance between the antennas and the length of cable between them will then govern the direction in which they radiate, or from which they receive.

In Figure 16 two dipoles A and B are a distance a apart and, while A is fed directly from the circuit, B receives the signal after passing through a delay line of length ℓ. At a point C in line with A and B the signal will have travelled a

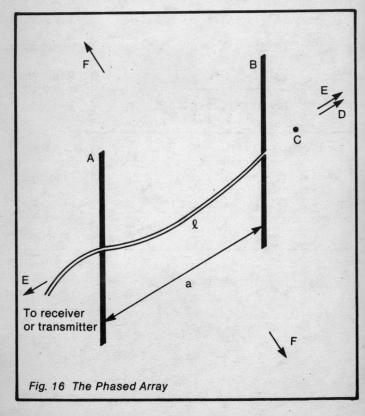

Fig. 16 The Phased Array

distance (ℓ − a) further from antenna A than it has from B. If (ℓ − a) is equal to a whole number of wavelengths the signals will reinforce one another in the direction of C. If (ℓ − a) is equal to an exact number of **half** wavelengths the signals will then cancel one another in the direction of C.

By choosing ℓ and a, the direction of the maximum emitted or received signal can be selected. Table 16.1 below, shows some "ℓ" and "a" values with the consequent directions of reception or transmission.

The many and various forms of phased array are discussed more fully by E. M. Noll in his book "25 Simple Amateur Band Aerials" (BP125) published by Bernard Babani (publishing) Ltd in 1983.

Table 16.1

Length in terms of λ		Direction of transmission or reception
a	ℓ	
$\lambda/4$	$\lambda/4$	→ D
$\lambda/4$	$\lambda/2$	E ← → E
$\lambda/2$	λ	↑ F ↓ F

17. Reflecting Elements

The addition of a reflector to an antenna concentrates the emitted or received radiation into a smaller angle. This improves the gain but, as it changes the radiation resistance of the antenna as well, it will also alter the efficiency.

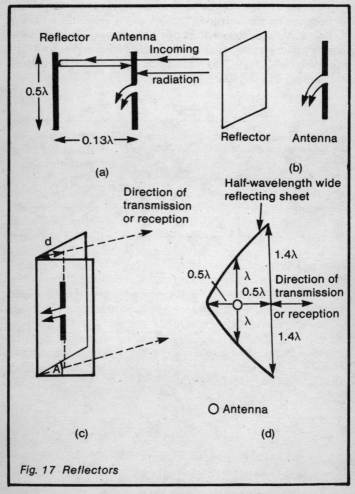

Fig. 17 Reflectors

The reflector can be either tuned or aperiodic. The typical tuned reflector is a 0.5λ long rod set around 0.13λ behind the antenna, as shown in Figure 17(a). The rod and the antenna both have currents excited in them and the two radiations from these two currents co-operate to reinforce forward radiation, or reception, according to whether the antenna is transmitting or receiving.

The aperiodic reflector is in effect a large metallic surface acting on the radio-signal much as a mirror would on visible light. In its simplest form it consists of a flat sheet of metal replacing the tuned rod behind the antenna, see Figure 17(b). The dimensions of the sheet are not critical, even a half-wavelength square has an effect and the reflector may be made from a wire mesh, provided the mesh dimensions are much smaller than a wavelength.

The corner reflector is a more elaborate and effective structure. It consists of two sheets of reflecting metal set at an angle A, as shown in Figure 17(c), with a half-wave dipole set symmetrically a distance d from the apex of the sheets. The reflecting sheets should be about two wavelengths tall and one wavelength wide. They can be cheaply made from cardboard from grocery cartons covered with cooking foil.

The performance of the corner reflector depends on the adjustment of A and d. The efficiency and gain both vary with these two factors and the best values must be found experimentally, starting perhaps with A~ 90° and d ~ 0.5λ.

The most effective reflector for a communication system between two fixed points is the dish seen in microwave links and satellite TV installations. Although dish construction is rather specialised, what in effect is the section of a dish, can be made by bending a half-wavelength wide reflecting sheet into the form shown in Figure 17(d). A half-wave dipole antenna is placed at the position shown in the figure with its arms parallel to the reflecting sheet.

18. Refractive Index of Free Electron Layers

In Section 3 the various atmospheric layers carrying free electrons were treated either as transparent to, or as reflecting, radio waves. In this section a more detailed look at their behaviour is taken. The analysis is quite long but straight-forward.

The electric current J that flows in free space when a radio wave passes through it is related to the **absolute** dielectric constant ϵ_0 by the expression:

$$J = \epsilon_0 \, dE/dt$$

where dE/dt is the rate of change of the electric field in the radio wave. For a field of amplitude E_0 volts/metre and a frequency fHz the value of E at any time t is given by the equation:

$$E = E_0 \sin 2\pi ft .$$

Differentiating both sides of this equation with respect to time t gives:

$$dE/dt = 2\pi f E_0 \cos 2\pi ft .$$

From the above formulae it can be shown that:

$$J = \epsilon_0 \, 2\pi f E_0 \cos 2\pi ft .$$

In the presence of free electrons an additional current J_e flows and this current must be calculated. The force of an electron in an electric field due to its charge e will be:

$$E.e = E_0 \sin 2\pi ft .$$

By Newton's Law this is equal to the electron mass m multiplied by its acceleration d^2x/dt^2 in the direction of the electric field.

$$e \, E_0 \sin 2\pi ft = m d^2x/dt^2 .$$

Integrating both sides of his equation with respect to t gives the velocity dx/dt as:

$$\frac{dx}{dt} = \frac{e\,E_0\,\cos 2\pi ft}{2\pi mf}.$$

If the electron density in the layer is N per metre^3 then the current density J_e is given by:

$$J = -e\,N \times dx/dt$$

$$= -\frac{e^2 N\,E_0\,\cos 2\pi ft}{2\pi mf}.$$

We now have:

Total free space current $J = \epsilon_0\,2\pi fE_0\,\cos 2\pi ft$

Total current in electron layer:

$$(J + J_e) = \epsilon_0\,2\pi fE_0\,\cos 2\pi ft - \frac{Ne^2 E_0\,\cos 2\pi ft}{2\pi mf}$$

Using previous equations shows that the ratio of currents

$$\frac{(J + J_e)}{J} = \text{Ratio of absolute dielectric constants}$$

$$= \frac{\epsilon\epsilon_0}{\epsilon_0} = \epsilon \text{ the relative dielectric constant}$$

$$= 1 - \frac{Ne^2}{4\pi^2\,mf^2\,\epsilon_0}$$

Putting in the constants $= 1 - N\left(\dfrac{9}{f}\right)^2$

Now the refractive index μ of a material is equal to the square root of the relative dielectric constant and so for the free electron layer

$$\mu = \sqrt{1 - N(9/f)^2}$$

The refraction or bending that a radio wave will suffer when striking a free electron layer can now be determined by using Snell's Law:

$$\mu = \frac{\sin(\text{angle of incidence})}{\sin(\text{angle of refraction})}$$

See Figure 18.

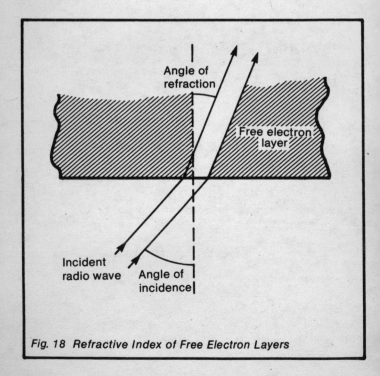

Fig. 18 *Refractive Index of Free Electron Layers*

If $N(9/f)^2$ is greater than 1, μ becomes imaginary and the layer is effectively transparent.

If $N(9/f)^2$ is less than 1 then Snell shows that radiation will be refracted but still pass through the layer unless the angle of incidence is greater than

$$\sin^{-1} \sqrt{1 - N(9/f)^2}$$

when it will be reflected back to earth.

19. The Skin Effect

Domestic t.v. antennas are often made from metal tubing rather than solid rods or wires. It seems at first sight that this would make the antenna elements into poor conductors, having only a thin shell of metal for the current flow. However, because of the phenomenon known as the "Skin Effect", the loss of conductance shown by a tube as compared with a rod can be very small at high frequencies.

If a direct current is passed along a wire it will flow uniformly through the entire cross-section whereas a radio-frequency current will be crowded into the outer skin as shown in Figure 19.

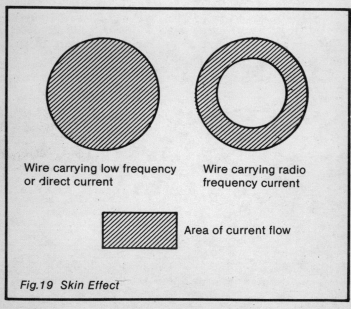

Wire carrying low frequency or direct current

Wire carrying radio frequency current

Area of current flow

Fig.19 Skin Effect

The higher the frequency of the current the thinner this skin becomes, while, at very low frequencies such as the 50 Hz of the domestic supply, the skin is so thick that the effect can be ignored.

To calculate the skin thickness t from the conductivity σ of the wire and the frequency f of the current the formula

$$t = \frac{0.5}{\sqrt{\sigma f}} \text{ metre}$$

can be used. Here f is measured in MHz and σ in siemens/metre. As an example a copper wire carrying a 10 MHz current would have a skin-depth of 0.02 millimetres.

The effect is also seen when radiation falls on a metal sheet. The depth of penetration of the radiation into the metal depends in the same way on the radiation frequency and the conductivity of the metal.

The cause of the skin effect lies in the magnetic field produced by a current-carrying wire. If the current is varying, then the magnetic field also varies and produces eddy-currents in the wire which oppose that part of the applied alternating current in the centre of the wire.

20. Sky Wave Antenna

A method has been reported for improving the signal given by a built-in whip antenna when receiving H.F. sky wave transmissions.

A horizontal loop of metal strip with the approximate dimensions shown in Figure 20 has a gap bridged by a 0.0005 μF variable capacitor. The receiver whip is laid across the loop but not in contact with it and its position, and the setting of the capacitor, are adjusted for maximum signal.

The loop is conveniently made with cooking foil stuck to the underside of a bench or work table.

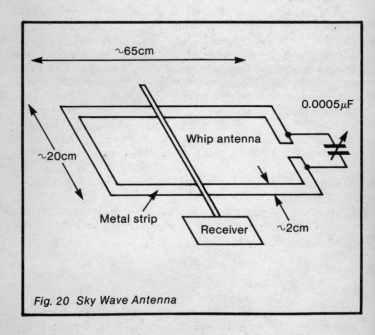

Fig. 20 Sky Wave Antenna

21. Standing Wave Interference in Domestic TV

(See the note heading Section 12)

In general a domestic TV antenna is required to receive eight different wavelengths to give sound and vision for four stations. For example the Sandy Heath Beds transmitter uses the following:

Station	Vision Frequency (MHz)	Sound Frequency (MHz)
Channel 4	471.25	477.25
ITV	495.25	501.25
BBC 2	519.25	525.25
BBC 1	551.25	557.25

giving a wavelength range from 0.64 to 0.54 metres. This gives no problem unless the signal is reflected from a nearby structure in which case the two radiations, direct and reflected, can interfere with one another. If the direct and reflected pathlengths differ by an exact number of half-wavelengths then the received signal will be reduced to a minimum. If they differ by an exact number of whole-wavelengths the signal will be a maximum.

In Figure 21(a) a remote transmitter T gives a direct signal to an antenna A and a second signal reflected off a structure R. If R is at a height h greater than A, and a distance r from it, then the vertical separation of maximum and minimum signal positions will be:

$$\frac{\lambda r}{2h}$$

If the antenna is moved horizontally towards or away from the transmitter the maxima and minima will be separated by

$$\frac{\lambda r}{2\sqrt{r^2 - h^2}}$$

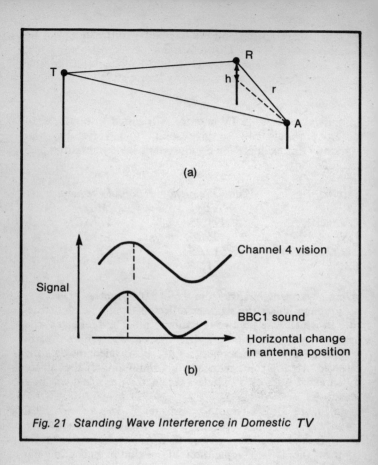

(a)

Channel 4 vision

Signal

BBC1 sound

Horizontal change
in antenna position

(b)

Fig. 21 Standing Wave Interference in Domestic TV

As an example let h = 10 and r = 50 metres then the
vertical separation is 2.5λ and the horizontal separation is
0.5λ. The extreme values calculated for the Sandy Heath
Channel 4 vision, and BBC 1 sound, max-to-min separations
are shown to scale in Figure 21(b).

With the maximum and minimum patterns of eight different wavelengths to satisfy, the positioning of the antenna to
give a maximum for them all can be a laborious business of
trial and error.

It is sometimes possible to locate the reflecting object by measuring the max-min distance and then calculating h/r, then finding a structure with a position that satisfies this ratio.

22. Substitutes for V.H.F. Whip Antennas

The whip antenna normally used on the V.H.F. domestic radio is inconvenient and sensitive to the movement of people in its vicinity.

Two compact substitutes have been developed for use in its place. The first, patented by the Royal Military College of Science consists of a normal ferrite rod as used in medium wave and long wave receivers with sets of reversed windings along its length as shown in Figure 22(a). After three or four turns in one direction the direction is reversed for another set of turns, all being wound from one continuous wire. Results using a rod about 1/22 of a wavelength long were reported as satisfactory for reception between 79 and 94 MHz. Exact tuning of the antenna was done by winding an excess of turns on the rod and then successively cutting turns off until the best performance was obtained. The report on this antenna suggests that all dimensions and even the rod materials are open to experiment for optimising the performance.

A different substitute for the whip has been examined by the B.B.C. Research Department. In this a rod of special high frequency ferrite (Neosid F29) which has very little loss up to 100 MHz is used in the manner similar to the ferrite rod antenna in medium and long wave radio. The tuning coil consists of three turns of wire, and the coupling coil of two turns. Figure 22(b) shows a schematic of the arrangement.

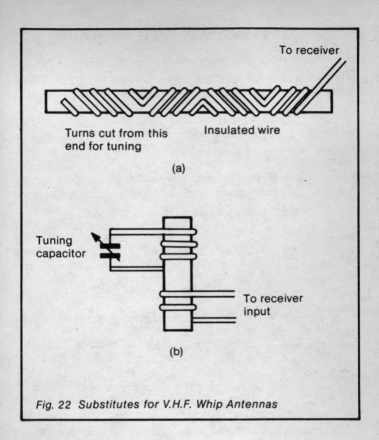

Fig. 22 Substitutes for V.H.F. Whip Antennas

23. Thermal Noise in the Antenna

The heat or thermal radiation which falls on an antenna from its surroundings produces a small alternating voltage in its output. This "noise" voltage in a simple dipole depends on:

ℓ the dipole length

λ the wave length

$(f_1 - f_2)$ the range of frequencies accepted by the antenna circuit

T the thermodynamic temperature of the antenna surroundings,

and the equation for the voltage V is:

$$V = 10^{-10} . (\ell/\lambda) \sqrt{T(f_1 - f_2)} \text{ volts.}$$

In practice the antenna will not be surrounded by a uniform temperature but will, for example, be subject to sky radiation with a temperature of $\sim 5°K$, horizon radiation at $100-150°K$ and ground radiation at $\sim 300°K$ and the noise temperature will take some average value, see Figure 23. This average will depend on the polar diagram of the antenna, the dominant value being the temperature of the region which the antenna "sees" most strongly.

To obtain the effective noise temperature of an antenna where the open circuit value of V is known, the above equation can be rearranged:

$$T = (10^{10} . V . \lambda/\ell)^2 / (f_1 - f_2) .$$

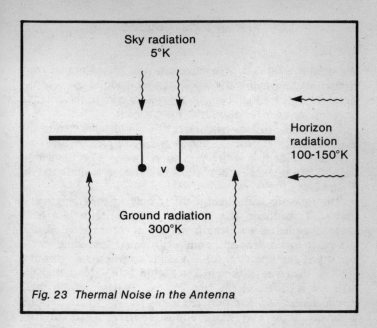

Fig. 23 Thermal Noise in the Antenna

24. Use of a Parasitic Element

A single straight rod or conducting wire placed near to, and parallel with, a half-wave dipole can be made to increase the signal collected either by guiding radiation onto the antenna or reflecting back radiation that has passed it.

This guiding or reflecting electrode is not connected to the antenna circuit electrically and so is called a parasitic element. Used as a guide it is a director and, if used to reflect radiation back to the antenna, it is of course a reflector, as illustrated in Figure 24(a).

The reflector and director differ only in their length and their distance from the antenna. The reflector is a little longer than half a wavelength and the director a little shorter, the exact amount for optimum performance depending on the parasite-to-antenna distance. A guide to parasite lengths and antenna distances is sketched in Figure 24(b). Note that the scale for h differs in the two graphs. It is seen from these that a change of a few per cent in the parasite length can turn a director into a reflector and vice-versa. Alternatively a parasite of a given length will direct or reflect according to the signal wavelength.

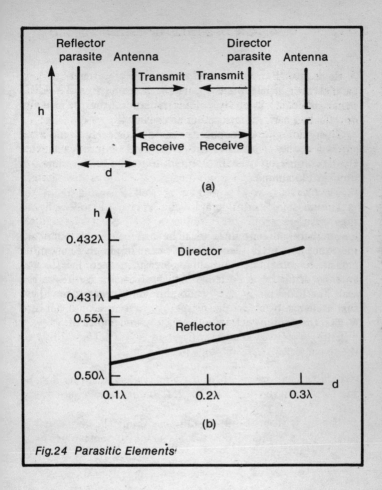

Fig.24 Parasitic Elements

61

25. Using the Pattern of TV Signal Maxima

Due to intereference the signal strength of terrestrial TV in most areas forms a regular pattern of maxima as the sketch in Figure 25(a) suggests. This pattern can be mapped out using a half-wave dipole antenna connected to a domestic TV receiver. The searching antenna can conveniently be mounted on the end of a broom-stick to minimise interference from the operator's body, and swept in a regular path to locate a number of maxima.

By placing several antennas at well separated points of maximum signal, considerable power may be collected, see Figure 25(b).

The array of antennas must be matched to the standard 75 ohm input of the receiver. If, for example, three antennas are to be used, each should be designed according to the section "Multi Loop Antennas" to have a radiation resistance of 200 to 250 ohms. The leads should also match and these can be made from parallel wires of radius r set a distance d apart. They will have a radio frequency impedance of

$$276 \cdot \log_{10}(d/r) \text{ ohms} .$$

Generally r will be fixed by the wire available leaving d to be adjusted to give the 200 to 250 ohm value required, see Figure 25(c).

The leads from the three antennas should be connected in parallel to a standard co-ax cable going to the t.v. receiver.

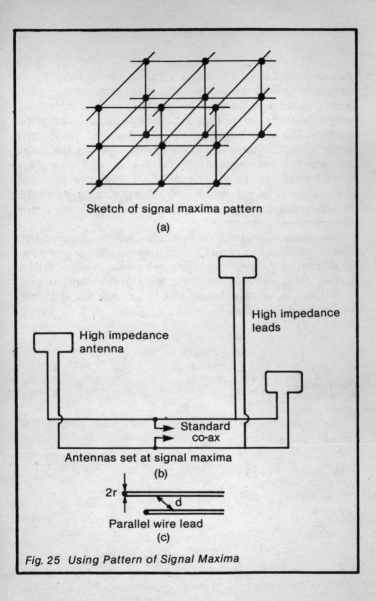

Sketch of signal maxima pattern

(a)

High impedance leads

High impedance antenna

Standard co-ax

Antennas set at signal maxima

(b)

$2r$

d

Parallel wire lead

(c)

Fig. 25 Using Pattern of Signal Maxima

26. Wave Traps

A single antenna can be made to serve two different wavelengths by making use of wave traps. In principle the overall length of the antenna is made suitable for the longer wavelength radiation and a break is made in it to give a length for use with the shorter wavelength. The break is bridged by a wave trap which must act like a switch, open to the longer wavelength signal and closed to the shorter, see Figure 26(a).

The wave trap can be formed by a capacitor C and an inductance L in parallel, Figure 26(b), making a rejector circuit tuned to impede, or reject, the higher frequency, shorter wavelength signal.

Dimensions for a dipole system to receive both 90 MHz and 600 MHz are shown in Figure 26(c). Each wave trap uses a 500 pF variable capacitor connected across a coil of 5 turns wound along a length of 5 cms on a 1 cm diameter tube.

As always, all dimensions should be regarded as starting points for experiment.

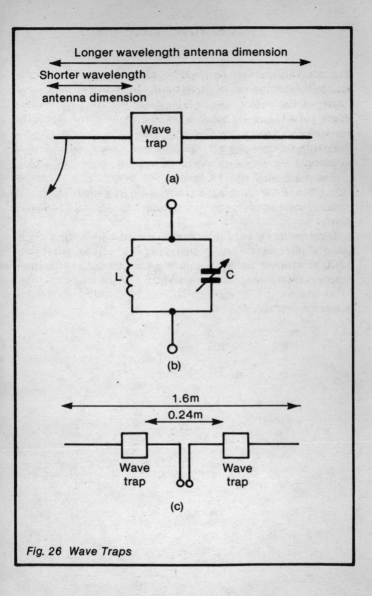

Fig. 26 Wave Traps

27. The Windom Antenna

The Windom is a very basic antenna consisting of a single wire or conducting rod with a lead tapped off part way along it. It can, nevertheless, give a signal voltage at least 80% of that from a standard half-wave dipole. Figure 27(a) shows the approximate dimensions of a Windom antenna which is to be operated at a wavelength λ. These dimensions should be taken as the starting point for experiment, particularly in the location of the tapping point A.

A method for making the antenna out of a single conductor without mechanical or electrical joints is suggested in Figure 27(b).

Figure 27(c) shows the dependance of the signal voltage, taken as the percentage of that given by a half-wave dipole, on the position of the tapping point A, when a Windom antenna was used to receive a 510 MHz TV signal.

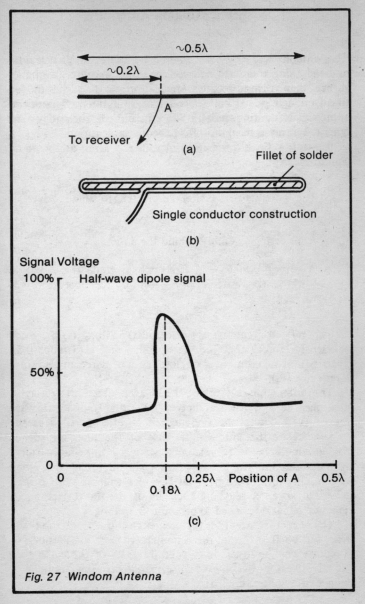

~0.5λ

~0.2λ

A

To receiver

(a)

Fillet of solder

Single conductor construction

(b)

Signal Voltage

100% Half-wave dipole signal

50%

0

0   0.18λ   0.25λ   Position of A   0.5λ

(c)

Fig. 27 Windom Antenna

67

28. Yagi-Uda Array

This antenna was originally devised by Professor Yagi and his student Uda to radiate and receive large amounts of energy rather than communicate information, and it did indeed beam enough power to charge a storage battery. The operation was interesting rather than efficient and nowadays the Yagi-Uda array is used only for telecommunication.

There are three basic elements in the array as shown in Figure 28(a):

(1) The antenna or exciter connected to the receiver or transmitter.

(2) A reflecting assembly behind the antenna.

(3) A set of directors in front which guide the radiation towards the antenna for reception or away from it for transmission.

The reflector can be a single rod 0.5λ long (i) or, more efficiently, three such rods set parallel and a distance 0.5λ apart (ii). A metallic sheet or close mesh of wire can also form a reflector (iii).

The antenna is set about 0.13λ away from the reflector and may be a half-wave dipole (iv), or a folded half-wave dipole (v). Since the presence of a reflector reduces the impedance of the antenna, the use of the high impedance folded dipole helps to restore a standard impedance value. A patented antenna recorded as giving a broad frequency response is in the form of an isosceles triangle with a 0.5λ base and an apex reaching back almost to the reflector (vi). The two equal sides need to be about 0.3λ long.

The directors are rods or elements about 0.4λ long, the first set at 0.3λ from the antenna (vii). Any number of directors can be used at further intervals of 0.3λ but each added director becomes less effective as the number is increased, see Figure 28(b).

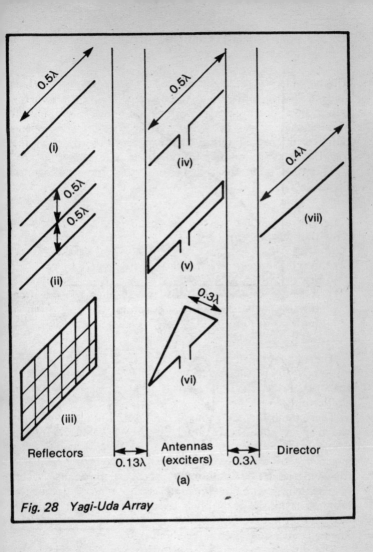

Fig. 28   Yagi-Uda Array

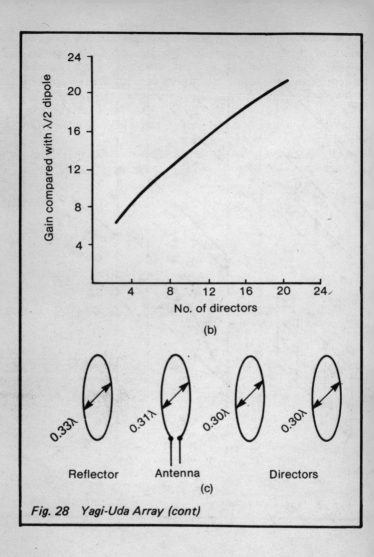

(b)

Reflector 0.33λ Antenna 0.31λ 0.30λ Directors 0.30λ

(c)

Fig. 28   Yagi-Uda Array (cont)

A variation of this form of array uses circular loops in place of the dipoles or mesh. The values for the loop diameters could be 0.33λ for the reflector, 0.31λ for the antenna and 0.30λ for the directors with the separations between elements being similar to those in the dipole array, this is illustrated in Figure 28(c). This form of Yagi-Uda array has been reported as showing a bigger gain than the more usual form.

All the element shapes, sizes and separations cited should be regarded as the starting points for experiment.

Other Books of Interest

If you would like a complete catalogue of our entire range of Radio, Electronics and Computer Books then please send a Stamped Addressed Envelope to:

BERNARD BABANI (publishing) LTD
THE GRAMPIANS
SHEPHERDS BUSH ROAD
LONDON W6 7NF
ENGLAND